DREAM TO WIN

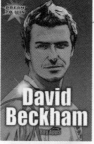

David Beckham
Roy Apps

978 0 7496 8232 3

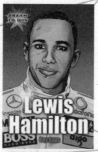

Lewis Hamilton
Roy Apps

978 0 7496 8233 0

Hope Powell
Roy Apps

978 0 7496 8235 4

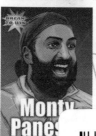

Monty Panesar
Roy Apps

978 0 7496 8

Wayne

Andy Murray
Roy Apps

0 7496 9027 4

Rebecca Adlington
Roy Apps

978 0 7496 9195 0

Chris Hoy
Roy Apps

978 0 7496 9196 7

Michael Phelps
Roy Apps

978 0 7496 9028 1

First published in 2010 by
Franklin Watts
338 Euston Road
London NW1 3BH

Franklin Watts Australia
Level 17/207 Kent Street
Sydney NSW 2000

A CIP catalogue record for this book
is available from the British Library.

ISBN: 978 0 7496 9550 7

Dewey Classification: 796.3'52'092

1 3 5 7 9 10 8 6 4 2

Printed in Great Britain

Franklin Watts is a division of Hachette Children's Books,
an Hachette UK company.
www.hachette.co.uk

Tiger Woods

Roy Apps

Illustrated by Chris King

LONDON·SYDNEY

Chapter One:

Baby Driver!

"I'm off now," Earl's wife Kultida called to him. "I won't be long. Just you make sure you take the baby somewhere nice. Like the park."

Every Saturday, Kultida went shopping and left Earl to look after their nine-month-old son, Eldrick. Every time she told Earl to take Eldrick to the park.

"You hear what I'm saying, honey?" said Kultida.

"Uh-huh."

Earl waited until he heard Kultida's car speed off down the road, then he went upstairs to Eldrick's room.

"Come on, you and me are going to the park," he told his son. "But first of all, we've got to go to the garage. I've got a golf match tomorrow and I need to put in some teeing off practice."

In the garage, Earl picked up a golf club and began to practise knocking golf balls into a net that was strung up on the back wall. Eldrick watched, fascinated. He never got tired of watching his dad balance himself on his feet and swing the club high through the air. It looked fun; it looked easy; it looked the sort of thing he would like to do.

So this particular Saturday, Eldrick clambered out of his little chair, picked up the toy golf club his father had given him as a present then, standing with his feet apart, swung the toy club and knocked a golf ball right into the middle of the net.

Earl stared in amazement at his young son. The boy had only just learned to walk, yet here he was, swinging a golf club like an old time professional.

"You're a natural," exclaimed Earl. "Reckon you could go a long way in this game, son."

Little Eldrick grinned.

"So what do you say… we go down the park or we stay here and play some more golf?"

In answer, Eldrick picked up his toy club and hit another ball towards the net.

Chapter Two:

Prejudice

When he was younger, Earl had been a Major in the US Army. While serving in Vietnam, his life had been saved by a Vietnamese soldier, Colonel Phong. He and Earl became great friends and Earl nicknamed him 'Tiger' because of his bravery and fierce determination.

After Earl left the army, his son Eldrick was
born. He started calling him 'Tiger', too, in
honour of his Vietnamese friend. It was a
good nickname; bravery and determination
were qualities that Tiger would need to help
him to become a top golfer.

Of course, while Tiger was still a toddler,
everything was exciting and so much fun.
He appeared on television to show off his
golfing skills, and the audiences cheered and
clapped at the little boy's feats with a golf
club. But he wasn't just a showbiz kid – he
loved playing golf.

Earl was a member of the local US Navy golf club. As a toddler, Tiger went along and played with him. Eventually, Tiger regularly went to play on his own.

One day, he was coming out of the clubhouse when a club official stepped out in front of him.

"And where do you think you're going, boy?" the man asked Tiger.

"To play a round of golf," replied Tiger.

The man laughed, cruelly. "Oh no, you're not! You're too young."

"But other boys my age play," protested Tiger.

By now a couple of other club officials had turned up.

"I was just telling Sergeant Brown's son here that he's too young to play," the first official told them with a sneer.

Tiger shuddered. He knew some of the white officers called his father 'Sergeant Brown'. 'Brown' because of the colour of his skin, 'Sergeant' because they believed no black person should become a Major in the US Army. He also knew it was no good trying to argue with men like these. Fighting back the tears, he headed home.

As the son of a black father and a Thai mother, Tiger was no stranger to racism. Indeed, on his very first day at school, a group of older, white boys grabbed hold of him and dragged him across the playground to the school field. There they tied him to a tree and started shouting racist abuse at him. But somehow, for Tiger, being banned from a golf course because of his colour seemed worse.

"How can I become a professional golfer if I'm not allowed to play?" he asked his father, angrily.

Earl put an arm round his son's shoulders. "Some people might not like it, but you will be allowed to play professional golf," he told Tiger, "because other black golfers have paved the way for you. Let me tell you about Charlie Sifford."

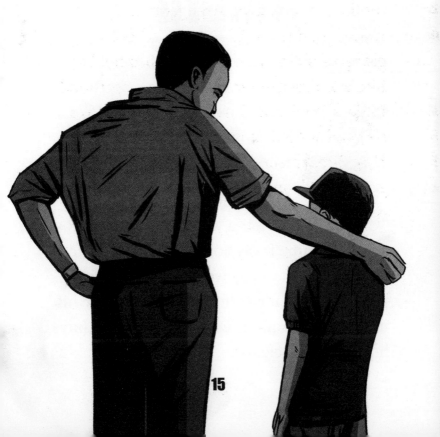

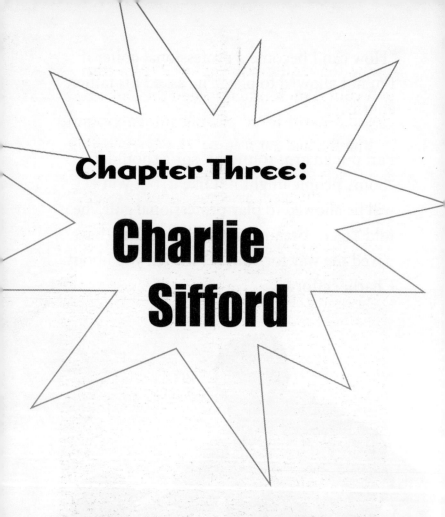

Chapter Three:

Charlie Sifford

"Charlie Sifford was a young kid in the 1930s, about the time I was born," began Earl. "He earned 60 cents a day working as a caddie at the local all-white country club. He'd give his mum 50 cents and keep 10 cents back to buy himself cheap cigars."

"Now, the caddies were allowed to use the golf course on Mondays when the club was closed. Charlie loved playing golf and found that he had a gift for it. He was helped by the club's owner. By the time he was thirteen, he could shoot par golf."

"Then, one day, the club's owner took Charlie aside and told him it might be best if he stayed away from the club. Charlie had got so good at golf that some of the club members didn't like it. They didn't think any black man should be better at golf than a white man. They'd told the club's owner that if Charlie didn't leave, he would get a good beating."

"So Charlie left the club and left home, determined to make his way in the world as a professional golfer. But the Professional Golfers' Association had a 'white only' rule. Charlie tried to ignore it, but without much luck. One time, he and three other black players reached the green on the first hole and found it filled with human poo."

"In 1960, Charlie took the Professional Golfers' Association to court and won. He became the first African American golfer to join the PGA Tour. But it still wasn't easy. During his first tournament, people phoned him at night, threatening to kill him if he showed up for the next round. Often he had to change his clothes in the car or eat in the locker room because, as a black man, he was still barred from the club changing rooms and restaurants. But he carried on playing and competing.

He won many tournaments, but was never allowed to compete in the biggest golf tournament of them all – the US Masters. The first African American to be allowed to play in the Masters was Lee Elder and that was only eight years ago, the year you were born."

Earl paused, then looked his young son steadily in the eye. "I guess you've got the talent to become a professional golfer. But have you got the determination and the bravery?"

Tiger nodded. "I'm going to become a professional golfer," said Tiger, firmly. "And I'm going to become the first mixed-race American to win the US Masters."

"Hey, that's some dream," said Earl, with a smile. "But I guess your mum and I didn't nickname you Tiger for nothing!"

Chapter Four:

Record Breaker!

After Tiger had been banned from the Navy course, his mum looked around to find somewhere else he could play. She discovered a public golf course at Long Beach called Heartwell. Rudy Duran, the club professional, took Tiger under his wing and the young golfer got better and better at his game.

By the time Tiger was fourteen, he had won five Junior World Golf titles. Aged fifteen, he won the first of his three record-breaking US Junior Amateur Championships. Aged seventeen, he won the Dial Award for best High School athlete in the US. He had been on television and had articles written about him in the newspapers. He was being trained by some of the country's top golf coaches.

Tiger knew that people saw him as someone special and expected great things from him, but sometimes he wondered if he could live up to all those expectations. He knew only too well that the sports world was full of people who had performed brilliantly as children or young teenagers, only for them to fade away when they reached adulthood.

In 1994, Tiger entered his first US Amateur Championship. He found the matches hard – after all he was the youngest player in the tournament. As a national event, it attracted lots of spectators and Tiger was conscious of the racist heckling in certain sections of the crowd. But he got through the early rounds and prepared himself for a tough final match. It was to be played against a friend of his, Trip Kuehne.

By the afternoon of the final day's play, Tiger was four strokes down and losing badly. He tried to concentrate, but he couldn't shut the crowd out. He fell so far behind, there didn't seem any way he could win the match.

"I've blown it," he muttered to himself, crossly. But somehow, believing he'd already lost the match took the pressure off him. He started to take risks with his shots; risks he would never have taken if he had been protecting a lead. Some of the risky shots worked. The crowd watched in amazement, while Trip Kuehne began to have doubts. With two holes left, Tiger was level.

The seventeenth hole was by a water feature. Most golfers worked their way around it, taking two or three shots. Tiger, though, was still in his daredevil mood. He hit his ball right across the reach of the water. The crowd gasped and watched as the ball seemed to hang in the sky. Would it drop into the water – or not? If it did, Tiger Woods would be penalised.

But the shot was so strong that the ball managed to clear the water. It bounced on the green and then started to roll back to the water! Luckily, it stopped just short. Tiger putted the ball into the seventeenth hole for a lead over Trip Kuehne that he held at the eighteenth to win him the match – and the championship.

Tiger's US Amateur Championship win meant he had an automatic invitation to play in the US Masters Tournament.

The US Masters was reserved for the world's very best golfers. It was the tournament Tiger had dreamed of winning, ever since his dad had told him the story of Charlie Sifford, the first black professional golfer.

Was Tiger's dream about to come true?

Chapter Five:

Burn Out

As the 1995 US Masters Tournament opened, the papers and television news channels were full of stories about Tiger Woods. Here was a young black man playing at the top level in a sport traditionally played by older, white men. Here was a young golfer who was very, very good. Many in the large crowd that gathered to watch the first day's play had come just to see Tiger Woods. And, more importantly, to see Tiger Woods win.

Tiger played well enough to reach the final rounds. There was a buzz of excitement around the famous Augusta National golf course. The media were ready to write their stories about another amazing Tiger Woods victory.

But it didn't happen.

Tiger played badly, finishing below par and way off the leaders. Some journalists wrote stories about how Tiger hadn't really got what it takes. Others were cross that he didn't give interviews after the match.

Given his age, Tiger's performance in his first US Masters was pretty good. But pretty good wasn't good enough for Tiger. He still had to prove himself and to do that he needed to play more golf. The following year he turned professional.

Being a professional meant Tiger was now busy doing adverts for his sponsors, giving interviews and making public appearances as well as playing golf. His game began to suffer. In some tournaments he played in, he wasn't even finishing with the leaders. Tiger knew that if he didn't get enough top placings, he'd lose his 'tour card'. And without a tour card, he wouldn't be able to compete in the Professional Golf Association tournaments the following year.

At the Buick Challenge in Pine Mountain, Georgia, Tiger shot a dreadful practice round. It was the first tournament he had played where he hadn't had either his dad or his coach there with him. Back at his hotel, he lay on his bed and stared up at the ceiling. He felt so lonely, so tired. All he wanted to do was go home to bed. He leaned over, picked up the phone and called reception.

"I'd like a taxi," he told the receptionist.
"To take me to the airport. Yep, that's right.
I'm checking out."

Tiger went home. He missed the tournament.
He also missed an awards dinner at which he
was to receive the award for the best college
golfer of the previous year.

The authorities – and journalists – were
furious. Tiger had to issue an apology.
Taking part in the 1997 US Masters, let
alone winning it, seemed a very long way
off indeed.

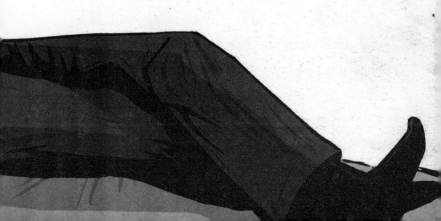

Chapter Six:

Winner!

Tiger rested. When he arrived for his next
tournament, which was in Las Vegas, he felt
a whole lot better.

He started off ordinarily enough, but as
the days went on, his golf improved and he
reached the last round where he tied with
another player, Davis Love III. Tiger and
Davis Love would have to play the eighteenth
hole in a sudden-death play off.

Tiger and Davis Love reached the green with Tiger one stroke up. Tiger needed to sink an eighteen-foot putt: tricky, but still not beyond Tiger's skills. He selected his club, steadied himself on his feet and swung. The ball trickled towards the hole, but stopped a couple of feet short. If Davis Love sunk his putt, they'd have to play another hole. But Davis Love hit his shot too hard and it rolled past the hole. Tiger had won his first PGA Tournament and with it a place at the 1997 US Masters!

Tiger played brilliantly in the first rounds of the Masters. But everybody knew that America's top golf event was notorious for the number of leaders who crashed out on the final day. That was what made it such an exciting tournament.

But Tiger was so determined that every shot worked for him. By the time he came onto the eighteenth green for his final putt, he had an incredible twelve-stroke lead over his nearest rival.

As he stood with his club in his hands, concentrating, everything was absolutely silent. Then came a 'tap' as Tiger stroked his ball toward the eighteenth hole. As soon as the ball slipped round the rim into the hole an almighty cheer erupted from the huge crowd.

Tiger Woods had won the Masters, 18-under-par, breaking a record that had stood for 32 years! He was the youngest ever Masters winner and, of course, the first African American winner.

After hugging his caddie and his father, Tiger turned to another person who had been allowed on to the green to watch his final putt – Lee Elder, the first African American to play at the US Masters, 20 years previously – the year Tiger was born.

Tiger hugged Lee. "Thanks," he said. The two men turned to the cameras and waved. They knew that among the millions watching the tournament at home on television was the man who had made it all possible, the man Earl Woods had told his young son about all those years ago: Charlie Sifford.

Full name: Eldrick Tont 'Tiger' Woods

Born: 30 December 1975

Place of birth: Cypress, California, USA

Height: 1.8 metres

1990	Wins the Optimist International Junior World title for the fifth time.
1994	Youngest player ever to win US Amateur Championship.
1996	Turns professional.
1997	Wins his first Masters Tournament – the first of four. Achieves No. 1 world ranking in his 42nd week as a professional. Becomes the youngest-ever No. 1 golfer (21 years, 24 weeks).
1999	Wins his first PGA Championship – the first of four.
2000	Wins British Open to become the youngest golfer to complete the Grand Slam of professional major golf championships and only the fifth ever to do so.
2001	Wins US Masters for the second time to become the first ever golfer to hold all four professional major championships at the same time.
2004	Sets record with 334 total weeks as No. 1 on the Official World Golf Ranking.
2005	First player to win PGA of America Player of the Year for seven years.
2007	Mark H. McCormack Award-winner as the No. 1 player on the 2007 Official World Golf Ranking for the seventh time.
2009	Selected US AP Athlete of the Decade.

Before the match begins the team mascot is allowed to have a few goes taking shots at the club goalkeeper.

Today's mascot watches the goalkeeper come off his line, then places the ball a little way outside the penalty area. His shot takes the goalie completely by surprise. It's a very high chip shot. The ball sails past the goalkeeper's outstretched hand and lands in the back of the net. The young mascot punches the air in triumph.

As he runs off the pitch, an announcement comes over the loudspeaker: "A big hand for today's Everton mascot, ten-year-old Wayne Rooney!"

**Continue reading this story in
DREAM TO WIN: Wayne Rooney**

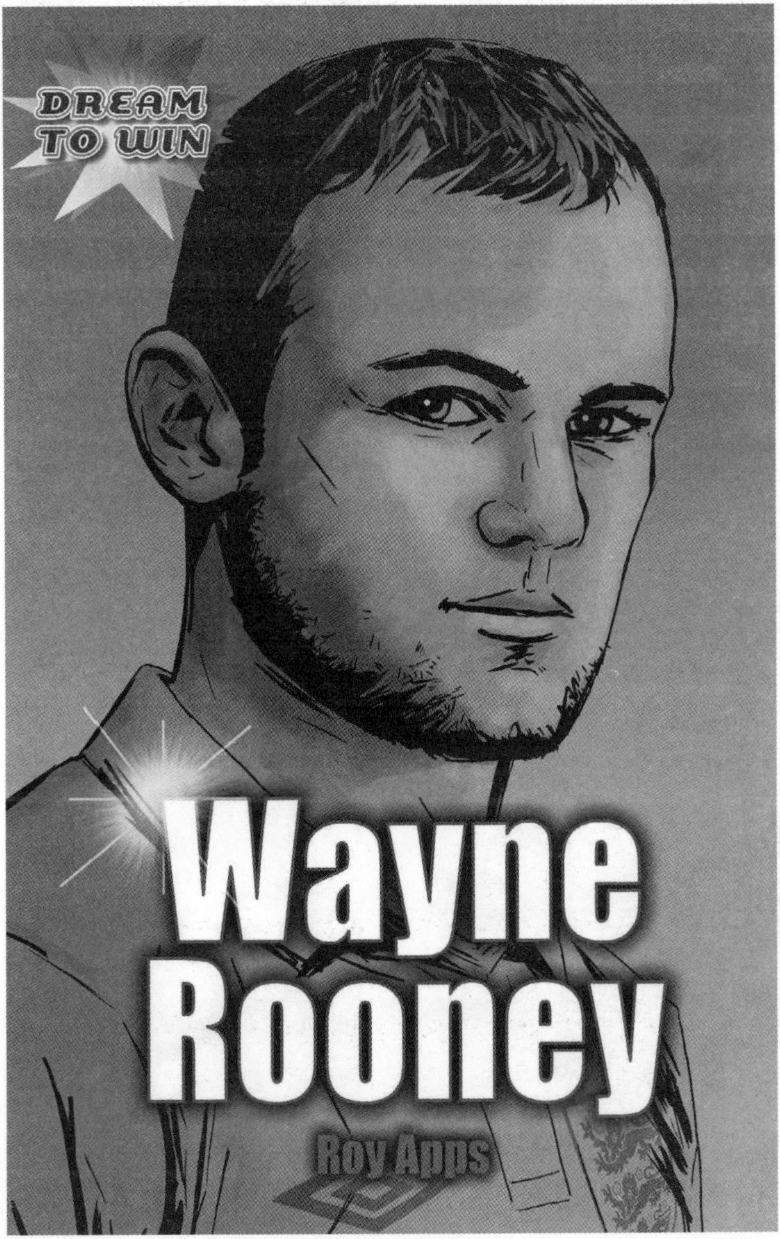
DREAM
TO WIN
Wayne
Rooney
Roy Apps

Also published by Franklin Watts:

978 0 7496 9286 5

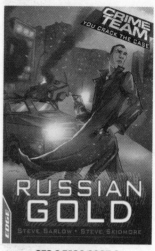

978 0 7496 9285 8

978 0 7496 9283 4

978 0 7496 9284 1